Buffy THE VAMPIRE SLAYER™

the ORIGIN

Buffy THE VAMPIRE SLAYER™
the ORIGIN

based on the television series created by

JOSS WHEDON
and adapted from his original screenplay

writers **CHRISTOPHER GOLDEN** and **DANIEL BRERETON**

penciller **JOE BENNETT**

inker **RICK KETCHAM** with **RANDY EMBERLIN** and **J. JADSEN**

colorists **JEROMY COX** with **GUY MAJOR**

letterer **KEN BRUZENAK**

photo cover artist **DAVE STEWART**

Titan Books

publisher

MIKE RICHARDSON

editors

SCOTT ALLIE *and* BEN ABERNATHY

designer

KRISTEN BURDA

art director

MARK COX

special thanks to

DEBBIE OLSHAN AT FOX LICENSING,

CAROLINE KALLAS AND GEROGE SNYDER AT *BUFFY THE VAMPIRE SLAYER*,

and DAVID CAMPITI AT GLASS HOUSE GRAPHICS.

published by TITAN BOOKS,
a division of Titan publishing Group Ltd.
144 Southwark Street
London SE1 0UP

September 1999
first edition
ISBN: 1 — 84023 — 105 - X

3 5 7 9 10 8 6 4 2

printed in Italy

THE ORIGIN

Art by JOE BENNETT and J. JADSEN

destiny free

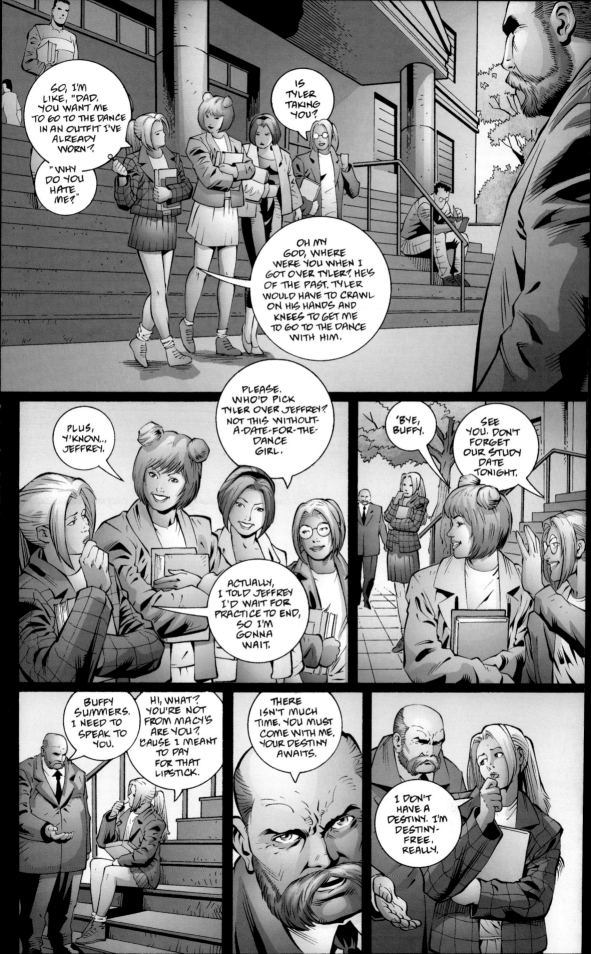

End of Issue One

defenseless MECHANISMS

THE ORIGIN

Art by JOE BENNETT and HECTOR GOMEZ

RIGHT. I'M THE CHOSEN ONE. AND I CHOOSE TO GO SHOPPING.

AH, I SHOULD'VE KNOWN. BENNY WAS RIGHT. YOU GUYS ARE ALL EXACTLY THE SAME--

--Y'KNOW THAT, BUFFY?

BUFFY? HER NAME IS BUFFY?

I RECOGNIZED HER LAST NIGHT. I KNOW HER FROM SCHOOL.

AND YOU KNOW WHERE SHE LIVES?

NO, MY LORD, BUT I KNOW WHAT SHE'S DOING ON SATURDAY NIGHT.

IT'S GOOD TO BE DEAD, BENNY. GOOD TO BE DEAD.

"THE DEATH TOLL NOW REACHES TWELVE-AND-A-HALF IN THE TRAGEDY AT HEMERY HIGH SCHOOL. A SENIOR DANCE WAS BEING HELD HERE IN THE GYM FIVE DAYS AGO, WHEN STUDENTS WERE ATTACKED BY A ROVING GANG OF CRACK-CRAZED GUNMEN,

"SURVIVORS SAY AT LEAST ONE HUNDRED OF THE RUFFIANS LAID THE HIGH SCHOOL UNDER A KIND OF SIEGE, CLAIMING SEVERAL LIVES IN THE PROCESS.

"SAID ONE SCHOOL ADMINISTRATOR, 'THINGS WILL NEVER BE THE SAME.'"

SHE WAS EVEN CRAZIER AFTER THAT.

I MEAN IT. YOU WOULDN'T EVEN HAVE RECOGNIZED HER.

BUFFY?

YEAH. SHE DIDN'T TALK TO ANYONE IN SCHOOL. THEN, OF COURSE, SHE GOT EXPELLED. THE WORST IS, HER PARENTS, AND THIS IS TRUE, I SWEAR--

THEY DIVORCED?

WELL, YEAH, BUT, NO, NO! LISTEN --HER PARENTS WERE GONNA SEND HER TO THE BAHAMAS FOR A WHILE, AND SHE REFUSED.

TRUE STORY.

SHE SAID SHE DIDN'T WANT TO GO.

IT IS TO VOMIT.

WELL, WHERE IS SHE NOW?

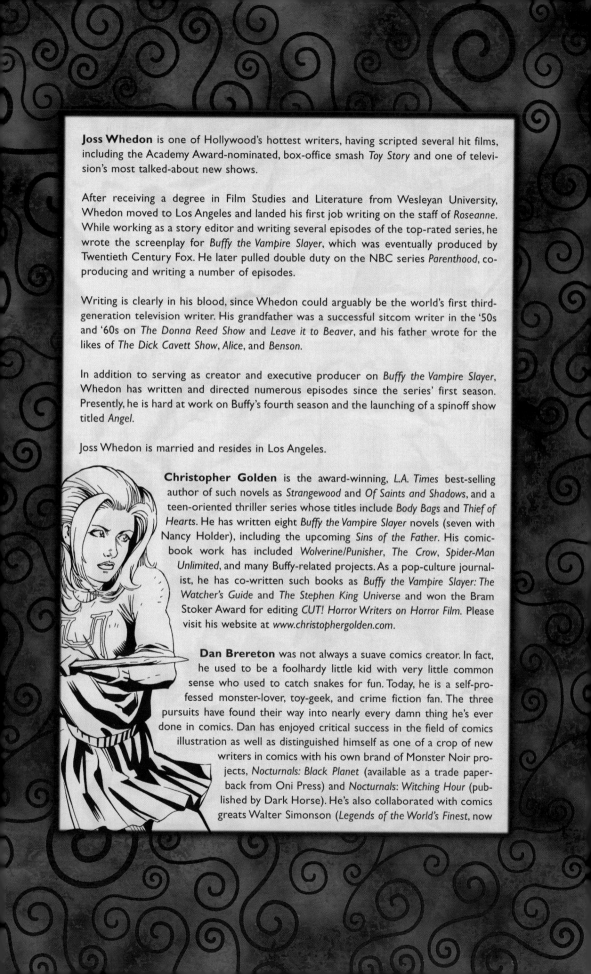

Joss Whedon is one of Hollywood's hottest writers, having scripted several hit films, including the Academy Award-nominated, box-office smash *Toy Story* and one of television's most talked-about new shows.

After receiving a degree in Film Studies and Literature from Wesleyan University, Whedon moved to Los Angeles and landed his first job writing on the staff of *Roseanne*. While working as a story editor and writing several episodes of the top-rated series, he wrote the screenplay for *Buffy the Vampire Slayer*, which was eventually produced by Twentieth Century Fox. He later pulled double duty on the NBC series *Parenthood*, co-producing and writing a number of episodes.

Writing is clearly in his blood, since Whedon could arguably be the world's first third-generation television writer. His grandfather was a successful sitcom writer in the '50s and '60s on *The Donna Reed Show* and *Leave it to Beaver*, and his father wrote for the likes of *The Dick Cavett Show*, *Alice*, and *Benson*.

In addition to serving as creator and executive producer on *Buffy the Vampire Slayer*, Whedon has written and directed numerous episodes since the series' first season. Presently, he is hard at work on Buffy's fourth season and the launching of a spinoff show titled *Angel*.

Joss Whedon is married and resides in Los Angeles.

Christopher Golden is the award-winning, *L.A. Times* best-selling author of such novels as *Strangewood* and *Of Saints and Shadows*, and a teen-oriented thriller series whose titles include *Body Bags* and *Thief of Hearts*. He has written eight *Buffy the Vampire Slayer* novels (seven with Nancy Holder), including the upcoming *Sins of the Father*. His comic-book work has included *Wolverine/Punisher*, *The Crow*, *Spider-Man Unlimited*, and many Buffy-related projects. As a pop-culture journalist, he has co-written such books as *Buffy the Vampire Slayer: The Watcher's Guide* and *The Stephen King Universe* and won the Bram Stoker Award for editing *CUT! Horror Writers on Horror Film*. Please visit his website at *www.christophergolden.com*.

Dan Brereton was not always a suave comics creator. In fact, he used to be a foolhardy little kid with very little common sense who used to catch snakes for fun. Today, he is a self-professed monster-lover, toy-geek, and crime fiction fan. The three pursuits have found their way into nearly every damn thing he's ever done in comics. Dan has enjoyed critical success in the field of comics illustration as well as distinguished himself as one of a crop of new writers in comics with his own brand of Monster Noir projects, *Nocturnals: Black Planet* (available as a trade paperback from Oni Press) and *Nocturnals: Witching Hour* (published by Dark Horse). He's also collaborated with comics greats Walter Simonson (*Legends of the World's Finest*, now

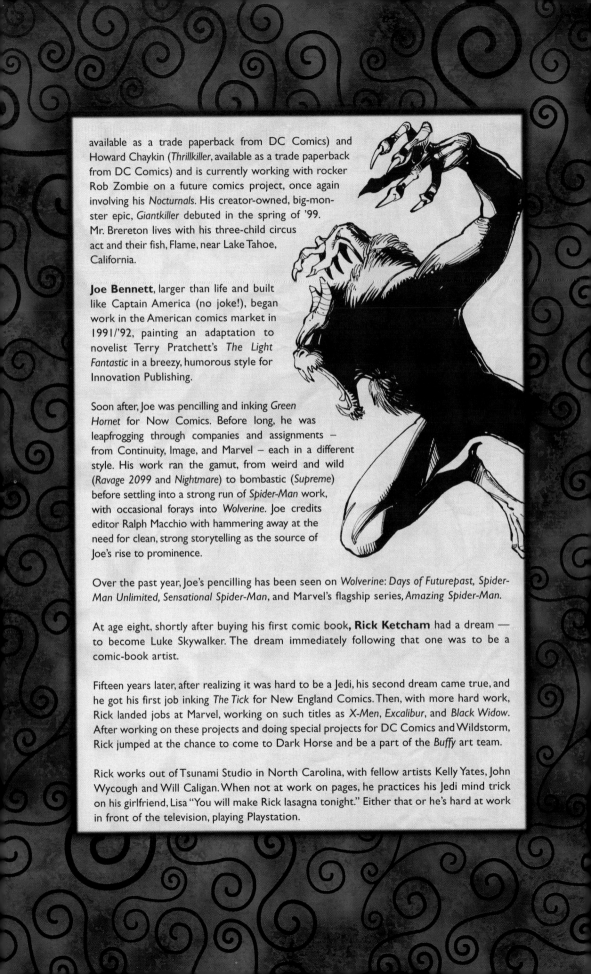

available as a trade paperback from DC Comics) and Howard Chaykin (*Thrillkiller*, available as a trade paperback from DC Comics) and is currently working with rocker Rob Zombie on a future comics project, once again involving his *Nocturnals*. His creator-owned, big-monster epic, *Giantkiller* debuted in the spring of '99. Mr. Brereton lives with his three-child circus act and their fish, Flame, near Lake Tahoe, California.

Joe Bennett, larger than life and built like Captain America (no joke!), began work in the American comics market in 1991/'92, painting an adaptation to novelist Terry Pratchett's *The Light Fantastic* in a breezy, humorous style for Innovation Publishing.

Soon after, Joe was pencilling and inking *Green Hornet* for Now Comics. Before long, he was leapfrogging through companies and assignments — from Continuity, Image, and Marvel — each in a different style. His work ran the gamut, from weird and wild (*Ravage 2099* and *Nightmare*) to bombastic (*Supreme*) before settling into a strong run of *Spider-Man* work, with occasional forays into *Wolverine*. Joe credits editor Ralph Macchio with hammering away at the need for clean, strong storytelling as the source of Joe's rise to prominence.

Over the past year, Joe's pencilling has been seen on *Wolverine: Days of Futurepast*, *Spider-Man Unlimited*, *Sensational Spider-Man*, and Marvel's flagship series, *Amazing Spider-Man*.

At age eight, shortly after buying his first comic book, **Rick Ketcham** had a dream — to become Luke Skywalker. The dream immediately following that one was to be a comic-book artist.

Fifteen years later, after realizing it was hard to be a Jedi, his second dream came true, and he got his first job inking *The Tick* for New England Comics. Then, with more hard work, Rick landed jobs at Marvel, working on such titles as *X-Men*, *Excalibur*, and *Black Widow*. After working on these projects and doing special projects for DC Comics and Wildstorm, Rick jumped at the chance to come to Dark Horse and be a part of the *Buffy* art team.

Rick works out of Tsunami Studio in North Carolina, with fellow artists Kelly Yates, John Wycough and Will Caligan. When not at work on pages, he practices his Jedi mind trick on his girlfriend, Lisa "You will make Rick lasagna tonight." Either that or he's hard at work in front of the television, playing Playstation.